BART SIMPSON 2011 ANNUAL

For information address
Bongo Comics Group
P.O. Box 1963, Santa Monica, CA 90406-1963, USA

Published in the UK by Titan Books, a division of Titan Publishing Group Ltd,
144 Southwark St., London SE1 0UP, under licence from Bongo Entertainment, Inc and Matt Groening Productions, Inc.

FIRST EDITION: AUGUST 2010
ISBN: 9781848568723
1 3 5 7 9 10 8 6 4 2

Publisher: Matt Groening
Creative Director: Bill Morrison
Managing Editor: Terry Delegeane
Director of Operations: Robert Zaugh
Art Director: Nathan Kane
Art Director Special Projects: Serban Cristescu
Production Manager: Christopher Ungar
Assistant Art Director: Chia-Hsien Jason Ho
Production/Design: Karen Bates, Nathan Hamill, Art Villanueva
Staff Artist: Mike Rote
Administration: Ruth Waytz, Pete Benson
Legal Guardian: Susan A. Grode

Contributing Artists:
Karen Bates, Tim Bavington, Mike DeCarlo, Serban Cristescu, Nathan Hamill, Tim Harkins,
Jason Ho, Mike Kazaleh, Jason Latour, Scott McRae, Bill Morrison, Phyllis Novin, Joey Nilges, Phil Ortiz,
Patrick Owsley, Andrew Pepoy, Ryan Rivette, Mike Rote, Art Villanueva, Mike Worley
Contributing Writers:
James W. Bates, Ian Boothby, Terry Delegeane, Evan Gore, Earl Kress, Michael Nobori,
David Razowsky, Eric Rogers, Jeff Rosenthal, Sherri Smith, Mary Trainor, Chris Yambar

PRINTED IN GERMANY

BART SIMPSON™
ANNUAL 2011

TITAN BOOKS

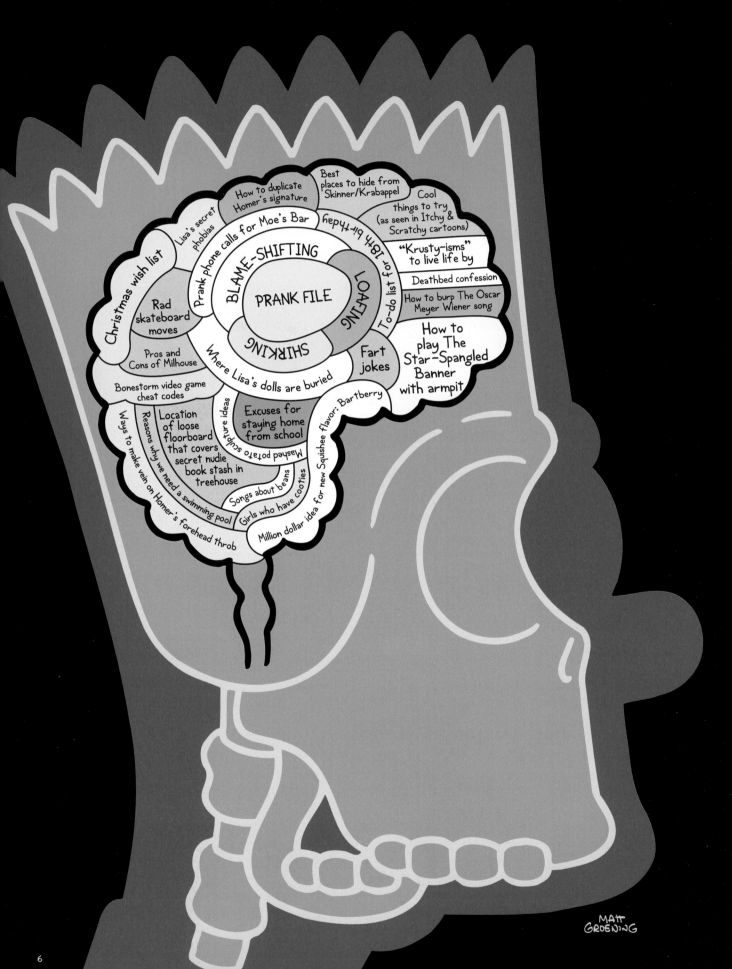

CHILDREN OFF THE COB

HEY, WHO'S THE NEW KID?

OH, THAT'S ETHAN ALL. HE JUST TRANSFERRED HERE FROM KANSAS.

MARY TRAINOR	**PHIL ORTIZ**	**MIKE DECARLO**	**NATHAN HAMILL**	**KAREN BATES**	**BILL MORRISON**
SCRIPT	PENCILS	INKS	COLORS	LETTERS	EDITOR

HEY, MILHOUSE. HOW'S IT GOING?

HI, ETHAN. I WANT YOU TO MEET MY BEST FRIEND AND WINGMAN, BART SIMPSON. BART, THIS IS ETHAN ALL.

HEY.

ETHAN ALL. ISN'T THAT THE STUFF THAT HIPPIES SQUEEZE OUT OF CORN?

CLOSE. YOU'RE THINKING OF ETHANOL.

SO WHAT DO KIDS DO FOR FUN IN KANSAS?

WE GROW CORN.

OOOOH... SOUNDS REAL CUTTING EDGE, DUDE.

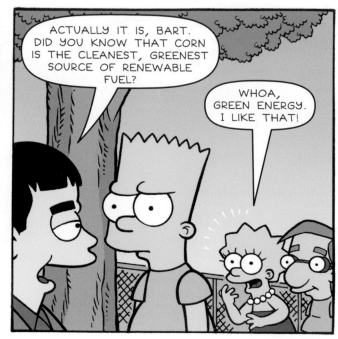

ACTUALLY IT IS, BART. DID YOU KNOW THAT CORN IS THE CLEANEST, GREENEST SOURCE OF RENEWABLE FUEL?

WHOA, GREEN ENERGY. I LIKE THAT!

AND DID YOU KNOW THAT WITH THE GREAT DEMAND FOR ALTERNATIVE FUEL, PLANTING CORN IS LIKE PLANTING MONEY TREES.

WHOA. GREENBACKS, I LIKE THAT!

SOON, HAVING A CORNFIELD WILL BE THE NEW STATUS SYMBOL. EVERYONE WILL BE WISHING THEY HAD ONE OF THEIR OWN!

WHOA, GREEN WITH ENVY. I LIKE THAT!

IT'S TRUE! IN THE PAST FEW YEARS, DOMESTIC PRODUCTION OF ETHANOL FROM CORN HAS MORE THAN DOUBLED!

WHOA, DOUBLED! WE LIKE THAT!

THAT'S RIGHT, ETHANOL PRODUCTION IS SKYROCKETING! HAVING A CORNFIELD IS LIKE HAVING AN ATM MACHINE IN YOUR BACKYARD!

KA-CHING!

9

SOON EVERY CHILD IN SPRINGFIELD IS TENDING A PLOT OF CORN IN THEIR BACK YARD.

THE CHILDREN ARE SO EXCITED BY THEIR NEW VENTURE THAT THEY BEGIN PLANTING CORN IN THEIR FRONT YARDS AND IN THEIR NEIGHBORS' YARDS, TOO.

LOOKING GOOD, DOLPH! ARE YOU SURE YOU'RE GIVING THE CORN ALL THE LOVE AND DEVOTION THAT IT NEEDS? BECAUSE YOU KNOW THE CORN LOVES YOU. AND YOU LOVE THE CORN.

DOLPH. LOVE. CORN.

LISTEN TO ME, WENDELL, YOU'RE NOT SICK SICK. YOU'RE JUST LOVE SICK. SICK WITH LOVE FOR THE CORN. UNDERSTAND?

MUST. LOVE. CORN. MUST. NOT. FEEL QUEASY.

THE PLANTING SOON SPREADS TO VACANT LOTS AND EVEN ONTO PUBLIC LAND.

BEFORE LONG, STALKS OF CORN GROW IN EVERY SQUARE FOOT OF OPEN SPACE IN SPRINGFIELD

I GOT IT! I GOT IT! I GOT IT!

GOT IT!

WHAT THE--?!

IS IT JUST ME OR ARE THINGS STARTING TO GET CREEPY AROUND HERE?

OH, WE'VE DEFINITELY CROSSED A LINE.

UH...ETHAN. CAN'T HELP BUT NOTICE THAT YOU'VE TAKING THIS WHOLE CORN THING IN A REALLY WEIRD DIRECTION...

A-HA! HE WHO CANS THE CORN SO PROPHESIED THAT UNBELIEVERS SHALL APPEAR AMONGST US. AND THESE UNBELIEVERS WILL PROFANE THE CORN.

OKAY. THAT'S IT. I'M OUT OF HERE, DUDE.

I'M RIGHT BEHIND YOU, BROTHER!

STOP THEM! DISOBEDIENCE TO ME IS DISOBEDIENCE TO HE WHO CANS THE CORN!

PUT THE UNBELIEVERS IN THE CORN SILO! THEY WILL DROWN IN THE SWEET KERNELS OF OUR FIRST HARVEST.

MUST. OBEY. CORN.

ETHAN ALL! ETHANOL! I TOLD YOU NO ONE NAMES THEIR KID AFTER CORN JUICE!

MEANWHILE, SPRINGFIELD IS OVERGROWN WITH FIELDS OF CORN.

HOO-BOY! ALL THIS YUMMY CORN IS AS HIGH AS AN ELEPHANT'S EYE, AND IT LOOKS LIKE IT'S CLIMBING CLEAR UP TO THE SKY!

MMMM... CORN DOGS...CORN CHIPS...CORN FLAKES.

POP CORN... CANDY CORN...OOOOH... A SCAREDY CROW!

A GROWN UP! SEIZE HIM! HE WHO CANS THE CORN COMMANDS THAT WE SACRIFICE A GROWN-UP!

MUST. KILL. GROWN-UP.

HEY! I'M JUST AS IMMATURE AS ANY ONE OF YOU PUNK KIDS!

WE WILL OFFER HIM UP TO HE WHO CANS THE CORN! IT IS WRITTEN THAT WE SHALL DO SO BY BOILING HIM IN A BIG VAT OF STEAMING CREAMED CORN.

MMM... CREAMED CORN.

GROUNDSKEEPER WILLIE BEGINS TO PLOW UNDER ALL THE CORNFIELDS IN SPRINGFIELD.

AND AS EACH STALK OF CORN FALLS, THE SPELL BEGINS TO LIFT.

MUST. OBEY. CORN. OBEY... MUST...

MUST...MUST. SEE. TV. SORRY, ETHAN. GOTTA RUN. IT'S TIME FOR "ITCHY AND SCRATCHY"!

¡OOOOF!¡

HEY! WAIT!

STOP! I COMMAND YOU TO COME BACK! THE CORN LOVES YOU!!!

Li'L KRUSTY

MARY TRAINOR
SCRIPT

JASON HO
PENCILS

MIKE ROTE
INKS

NATHAN HAMILL
COLORS

KAREN BATES
LETTERS

BILL MORRISON
EDITOR

12 ANGRY KIDS

NOOOO!

WHAT'S WRONG, SEYMOUR?

SOMEONE PICKED THE LOCK TO MY OFFICE DOOR AND STOLE MY COLLECTION OF WAR MEDALS!

NELSON MUNTZ!

HUH?

GIVE ME BACK MY WAR MEDALS!

WHAT?

DON'T PLAY DUMB. I KNOW YOU TOOK THEM.

JAMES W. BATES
SCRIPT

MIKE KAZALEH
PENCILS

PHYLLIS NOVIN
INKS

ART VILLANUEVA
COLORS

KAREN BATES
LETTERS

BILL MORRISON
EDITOR

A FEW HOURS LATER AFTER THE PROSECUTION AND THE DEFENSE HAVE RESTED...

NOW THAT WE'VE HEARD THE CASE, IT'S TIME FOR THE JURY TO DELIBERATE.

JURORS, IN ORDER TO RETURN A VERDICT OF "GUILTY," YOU MUST BELIEVE *BEYOND A REASONABLE DOUBT* THAT NELSON DID IT.

YOUR VOTES ON THIS ARE VERY IMPORTANT. "AMERICAN IDOL" IMPORTANT! NOW GO AND DON'T RETURN UNTIL YOU HAVE A UNANIMOUS DECISION.

TEACHERS LOUNGE JURY ROOM

PLEASE, EVERYONE TAKE A SEAT.

JURY ROOM

YEAH. I WANT TO GET THIS OVER WITH.

FOREMAN

SOMEONE'S CRUISIN' FOR A BRUISIN'.

LISA, DO YOU REALLY THINK NELSON IS *INNOCENT*?

I'M NOT SURE.

WE'RE TALKING ABOUT A YOUNG MAN'S EDUCATION. WE OWE IT TO HIM TO TALK IT THROUGH AS LONG AS THERE IS A REASONABLE DOUBT. WHAT IF YOU'RE ALL WRONG?

I GUESS A LITTLE DISCOURSE WOULDN'T HURT.

FOREMAN

I SAY THAT CONVERSATION SHOULD BE ABOUT FEEDING LISA A KNUCKLE SANDWICH.

I HAVE MORE THAN A REASONABLE DOUBT THAT WE'D BULLY A GIRL. WE'RE NOT ANIMALS!

OH. RIGHT.

WE CAN'T GET THE GIRL, BUT HOW ABOUT HER BROTHER?

HUH?

BUT I'M ON *YOUR* SIDE!

27

HAVE I MADE MY POINT THAT NELSON HAVING A BURGLAR BUDDY PROVES *NOTHING*?

YOU HAVEN'T PROVED THAT HE *DIDN'T* DO IT!

BUT THERE'S *REASONABLE DOUBT*.

IT'S STILL ELEVEN TO ONE.

IS IT? LET'S TAKE ANOTHER VOTE. IF EVERY-ONE ELSE STILL AGREES, I'LL GO ALONG AND VOTE "GUILTY."

RAISE YOUR HAND IF YOU VOTE "NOT GUILTY."

NELSON'S PROBABLY GUILTY, BUT WE MUST FACTOR IN THE VARIABLES.

YOU KNOW WHAT THIS MEANS.

D'OH!

COULDN'T YOU STOP BEING SO STUBBORN AND JUST GIVE IN?

THAT WOULD BE WRONG. THE OTHERS JUST WANT TO GET THIS OVER WITH BECAUSE THEY'RE BORED.

FOREMAN

WHAT IF WE VOTE WITH YOU, AND NELSON REALLY *DID* STEAL THOSE MEDALS?

MAYBE I **SHOULD** GIVE IN.

UGH! THEY REALLY AREN'T TAKING THIS SERIOUSLY.

WE'RE NOT GETTING OUT OF HERE ANYTIME SOON, SO I'M READY TO ADMIT THAT LISA HAS A POINT.

WHAT?

I'M CHANGING MY VOTE TO "**NOT** GUILTY!"

HMM...

MAYBE IT WAS WILLIE! HE'D STEAL THOSE MEDALS JUST TO CHEESE OFF SKINNER, **AND** HE HAS A MASTER KEY!

NOT GUILTY!

ME, TOO! **NOT** GUILTY!

YEAH, YEAH! WHAT ELSE CAN YOU DO TO ME?

THAT MAKES IT FIVE TO SEVEN.

SIX TO SIX. I *CAN'T* GO AGAINST MY SISTER.

HOW IS IT GOING?

IT'S SIX TO SIX. PLEASE TELL PRINCIPAL SKINNER IT'S A HUNG JURY.

NAH...I THINK YOU CHILDREN NEED TO WORK A LITTLE LONGER.

FOREMAN

BUT THE FACT THAT YOU KNOW WHAT A HUNG JURY IS MAKES ME SO HAPPY. MAYBE I HAVEN'T WASTED MY LIFE BY TEACHING.

FOREMAN

WE'RE SPLIT FIFTY-FIFTY NOW. WE *CAN'T* CONVICT AND CONDEMN NELSON TO EXPULSION. HIS CRIME *WASN'T* PROVEN BEYOND A REASONABLE DOUBT!

LET'S VOTE AGAIN.

FOREMAN

THE END

OH, SURE. *YOU* ONLY GOT A LITTLE ON THE *FACE*. I GOT IT IN MY HAIR!

HEY, IT COULD BE *WORSE*. IT COULD BE *SCHOOL PICTURE DAY*.

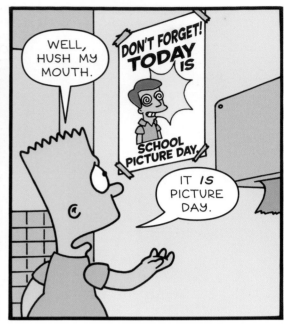

WELL, HUSH MY MOUTH.

DON'T FORGET! TODAY IS
SCHOOL PICTURE DAY.

IT *IS* PICTURE DAY.

OH NO! I EVEN GOT IT IN MY EYE-BROWS. MY *BEAUTIFUL EYEBROWS!*

CHILL OUT. IT'S JUST A LITTLE GUM.

YOU DON'T KNOW MY *PAIN!* YOU DON'T EVEN *HAVE* EYE-BROWS!

LET'S NOT START COMPARING WHO'S GOT HAIR WHERE. IT JUST SO HAPPENS, I KNOW SOMEONE WHO CAN HELP YOU.

MONSIEUR MEAL-HOUSE, I, ZEE GREAT JEAN-BART, *HAIRSTYLEAST* TO ZEE *STARS*, WILL GIVE YOU ZEE *PEAR-FECT AMERICAN HAIRCUT*.

NO WAY, BART. YOU HAVE TROUBLE CUTTING A *SAND-WICH* IN HALF.

WHAT COULD I *POSSIBLY* DO THAT WOULD MAKE THAT *WORSE*?

UHHH, BART, I DON'T...

SIT BACK AND PREPARE TO BE *DAZZLED!*

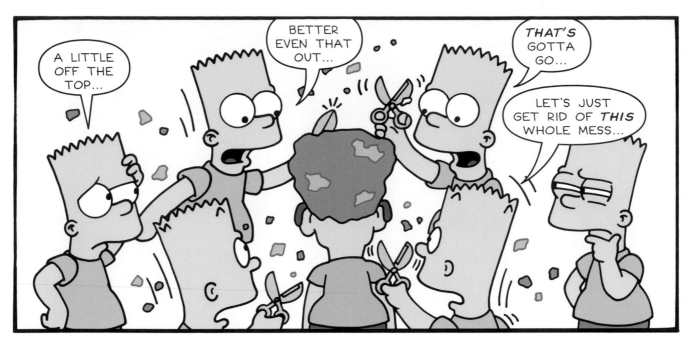

I'VE LEARNED, IF YOU MAKE A **MISTAKE,** THE BEST THING TO DO IS **COVER** IT UP. IT WORKS FOR POLITICIANS ALL THE TIME.

HOW ABOUT GOING **OLD SCHOOL**? TRY THIS ONE.

UHHH, I THINK I GET **BEAT UP** ENOUGH **ALREADY.**

COOL! A REAL COONSKIN CAP.

YEAH, IT MAKES ME FEEL LIKE A RUGGED MOUNTAIN MAN.

SPROING!

WAAAH!

GET ME OUT OF HERE! IT SMELLS LIKE A SAILOR'S BUTT!

WHAT ARE YOU GETTING ALL **WEEPY** ABOUT?

A BOY CAN **DREAM,** CAN'T HE?

LI'L KRUSTY

MARY TRAINOR
SCRIPT

JASON HO
PENCILS

MIKE ROTE
INKS

NATHAN HAMILL
COLORS

KAREN BATES
LETTERS

BILL MORRISON
EDITOR

CHRIS YAMBAR
SCRIPT

MIKE WORLEY
PENCILS

MIKE ROTE
INKS

KAREN BATES
COLORS/LETTERS

BILL MORRISON
EDITOR

MATT GROENING
SLUSH-BALL KING

THE END

42

CHRIS YAMBAR
SCRIPT

RYAN RIVETTE
PENCILS

ANDREW PEPOY
INKS

JASON LATOUR
COLORS

KAREN BATES
LETTERS

BILL MORRISON
EDITOR

MATT GROENING
KING OF KAIJU

GLOMPH!

I SUPPOSE OL' WILLIE WILL BE GOING TO THE BEACH TODAY AFTER ALL. *YAHOO!*

AS BARTZILLA TAKES A LUNCH BREAK DURING HIS RAMPAGE THROUGH SPRINGFIELD, THERE SEEMS TO BE NO WAY OF STOPPING HIM OR THE CITIZENS WHO HAVE GATHERED FOR PHOTO OPPORTUNITIES AND POSSIBLE AUTOGRAPHS.

YOU WILL BE WORKING OFF THAT SQUISHEE MACHINE FOR MANY MONTHS, YOUNG SIMPSON!

CAN YOU MAKE IT OUT TO "MY SPECIAL FRIEND, NELSON"? THAT WOULD BE *SO* COOL!

FINALLY. SOMEONE WHO HAS *BIGGER FEET* THAN ME!

CUFF HIM, BOYS!

UH...*YOU* CUFF HIM, CHIEF!

CAUTION·POLICE·CAUTION·POLICE·CAUTION·POLICE

WHOOOOOOM!

BARTZILLA HAS JUST UNLEASHED HIS *NUCLEAR FIRE BREATH* AGAINST THE NEWCOMER.

B-ZAAAP!

"BUT HIS ATTACK IS MET WITH AN INCREDIBLE *EYE-BEAM BLAST* FROM ROBO-SIS."

I'M THINKING OF PRESSING CHARGES.

"BARTZILLA HAS BEGUN TO HURL CARS, MONUMENTS, AND CITIZENS AT HIS OPPONENT, CATCHING HER OFF-GUARD."

GREAT! HERE'S MY CARD. CALL ME IN THE MORNING.

BUT ROBO-SIS FIGHTS ON WITH PROPS OF HER OWN! MOST IMPRESSIVE!

YOINK!

DOINK!

IT SEEMS THESE GIANTS ARE ONLY GETTING **WARMED UP**. WILL ANYTHING BE LEFT STANDING WHEN THEY ARE FINISHED? CAN **EARTH** SURVIVE? CAN **ANYTHING** STOP THEM?!!

BART! LISA! STOP **FIGHTING**, RIGHT NOW!

UH-OH!

WHAT IN THE WORLD ARE YOU TWO THINKING?

UMMM...

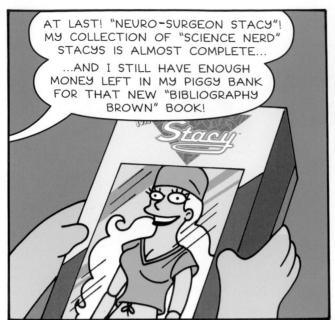

THE CASE OF THE HEADLESS DOLLS

EARL KRESS
TERRY DELEGEANE
SCRIPT

PHIL ORTIZ
PENCILS

PATRICK OWSLEY
INKS

ART VILLANUEVA
COLORS

KAREN BATES
LETTERS

BILL MORRISON
EDITOR

YOU SHRIEKED?

HOW MANY TIMES HAVE I TOLD YOU TO LEAVE MY DOLLS ALONE?

I DON'T KNOW. WAS I SUPPOSED TO KEEP COUNT?

GRRR!

HOW DO YOU EXPLAIN *THIS*!? ARE YOU TELLING ME THAT *ROCKET SCIENTIST STACY'S HEAD* DISAPPEARED ALL BY ITSELF?

I 'UNNO. *SHE'S* THE ROCKET SCIENTIST. ASK *HER*!

YOU HAVEN'T HEARD THE LAST OF THIS!

YES, I HAVE, 'CAUSE I AM *OUTTA HERE*!

CLOMP!

BA-DOMP!

JUST YOU WAIT, BART SIMPSON. I'LL GET TO THE BOTTOM OF THIS!

THIS LOOKS LIKE A JOB FOR SUPER-SLEUTH STACY.

COME ON, SANTA'S LITTLE HELPER, YOU CAN HELP US FIND OUR HEADS!

53

LATER THAT NIGHT...

HOLD IT RIGHT THERE, BART!

WHUH!

ŧHEH, HEHŧ SO MUCH FOR *THE ELEMENT OF SURPRISE*. HOW LONG HAVE YOU BEEN WAITING FOR ME?

THAT'S NONE OF YOUR BUSINESS, BART!

THOUGH I THINK I MUST HAVE FALLEN ASLEEP--

HEY, WAIT A MINUTE! THIS IS *MY* INVESTIGATION.

WHAT'S ON YOUR MIND, BATGIRL?

J'ACCUSE!

WHAT ARE YOU TALKING ABOUT?

J'ACCUSE. IT'S *FRENCH*. IT MEANS "*I ACCUSE YOU*." ACTUALLY, STACY AND I ACCUSE YOU, SO IT SHOULD REALLY BE "NOUS T'ACCUSONS," BUT THAT'S JUST THE LITERAL--

LISA, JUST TELL ME WHAT YOU THINK I DID!

YOU DECAPTITATED ALL MY MALIBU STACYS, JUST LIKE YOU DID TO YOUR SUPERHERO ACTION FIGURES.

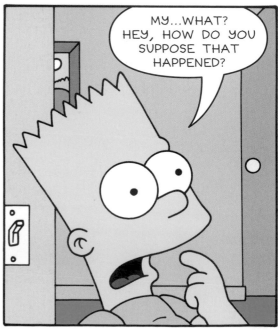

MY...WHAT? HEY, HOW DO YOU SUPPOSE THAT HAPPENED?

55

Li'L KRUSTY

MARY TRAINOR
SCRIPT

JASON HO
PENCILS

MIKE ROTE
INKS

NATHAN HAMILL
COLORS

KAREN BATES
LETTERS

BILL MORRISON
EDITOR

COOL, MY *KRUSTY BALLOON ANIMAL SCULPTING KIT'S* FINALLY HERE. AT LAST, I'LL BE AN *ARTIST.*

YOU, A BALLOON ARTIST? I'LL *BELIEVE* IT WHEN I *SEE* IT!

OH, YE OF LITTLE *FAITH.*

BALLOON PAYMENT

COOL! WHAT *ELSE* CAN YOU MAKE?

WATCH AND BE AMAZED!

HMMM... SOMETHING'S NOT *RIGHT.*

THIS *NEW SOFA* IS SO *COMFORTAMABLE!* LIKE A *CUSHION OF AIR!*

SQUEAK!

SQUEAK!

HOMER, I THINK BART'S *NEW HOBBY* IS BECOMING A *PROBLEM!* AND THIS *STATIC* IS RUINING MY HAIR!

CRACKLE!

CRACKLE!

SQUEAK!

SQUEAK!

SQUEAK!

BUT, MARGE, THE BOY SHOW'S *TALENT.* WE SHOULD *ENCOURAGE* HIM! AND *MY HAIR'S* WAVIER THAN IT'S BEEN IN *YEARS!*

SHERRI SMITH
SCRIPT

MIKE ROTE
PENCILS

SCOTT MCRAE
INKS

ART VILLANUEVA
COLORS

KAREN BATES
LETTERS

BILL MORRISON
EDITS

MATT GROENING
HOT AIR

GIVEN *FANTASTIC POWERS* DURING A *FREAK X-RAY ACCIDENT*...

CHILDREN! *DUCK AND COVER* LIKE WE DID DURING THOSE *FREAK X-RAY ACCIDENT DRILLS!*

KA-ZAP!

BART AND LISA SIMPSON BECAME...

STRETCH DUDE AND CLOBBER GIRL

LIKE, *OW!*

NOTHING CAN STOP *THE MINI MISS OF MIGHT* AND *THE RADICAL RUBBER REBEL* IN THEIR *WAR ON CRIME!*

NOTHING EXCEPT...

IF YOU'RE GOING OUT, TAKE *MAGGIE* WITH YOU.

BUT MOM!

IAN BOOTHBY
STORY

PHIL ORTIZ
PENCILS

TIM BAVINGTON
INKS

ART VILLANUEVA
COLORS

KAREN BATES
LETTERS

BILL MORRISON
EDITOR

MATT GROENING
FREAK ACCIDENT INVESTIGATOR

61

GIVEN **SUPERPOWERS** IN A **FREAK ELECTRIC CHAIR ACCIDENT**, CRIMINAL SUB-MASTERMIND SNAKE HAS BECOME **SNAKESKIN**...A VILLAIN WITH THE ABILITY TO **SHED HIS SKIN**, CREATING **PERFECT DUPLICATES!**

AND FROM THAT DAY FORTH ALL WAS WELL! **NOTHING** COULD STOP **THE TREMENDOUS TRIO** IN THEIR **CRUSADE AGAINST EVIL**.

NOTHING EXCEPT...

'NUFF SAID!

THE SIMPSONS

BONGO COMICS GROUP

Story: Gore, Razowsky, Rosenthal   Art: Ortiz/Harkins

WHEN DEALING WITH BULLIES, BRAINIACS AND BOSSY AUTHORITY FIGURES, THERE'S NOTHING LIKE A GOOD *CATCH PHRASE* TO DIFFUSE A DICEY SITUATION. MOST CATCH-PHRASES ARE EASY TO CREATE *ONCE* YOU KNOW *THE SECRET!* LET'S LOOK AT THIS *CLASSIC* EXAMPLE:

DON'T HAVE A COW, MAN!

THIS WORD, NORMALLY RESERVED FOR TEACHERS, MOMS AND KWIK-E-MART CLERKS, IS A SURE-FIRE TICKET TO CATCH-PHRASE HEAVEN. STARTING YOUR PHRASE WITH A 'COMMAND' TELLS THE LISTENER, '*LISTEN UP. SOMETHING'S COMIN'.*

THE VERY *CATCH* OF THIS *CATCH-PHRASE* ORIGINATED IN FARMING COMMUNITIES. IT EXPRESSES THE AGONY A COW GOES THROUGH DURING THE BIRTHING OF A CALF. IF YOU'VE EVER SEEN A RECENT VICTIM OF A SPITBALL TO THE HEAD OR A TEACHER WHO'S FELT THE COLD STEEL OF A TACK ON HER CHAIR, THEN YOU KNOW THEIR AGONY AND THE COW'S IS ONE AND THE

THOUGH THIS GROOVY ALL-PURPOSE MONIKER COMES FROM OUR *BEATNIK* FRIENDS OF A SIMPLER TIME, IT IS NO LESS USEFUL TODAY. IT REPRESENTS MANKIND AND APPEALS TO THE LISTENER'S HUMANITY. BUT COMING FROM A KID, IT ALWAYS SEEMS TO CHEESE OFF ADULTS, ESPECIALLY PRINCIPALS, TEACHERS, DOCTORS AND COPS.

COMMAND	CATCH	MONIKER
BE	(LIKE) A CRAB	SQUIRE
FISH	(IN) YOUR PANTS	YOUR HONOR
BITE	MY BUTT	MR./MRS.
SUCK	(WITH) AN EGG	DOC
FIGHT	THE POWER	SISTER
EAT	MY SHORTS	JACK
DON'T	(BLOW) A FUSE	HOME-BOY
GO	POSTAL	TEX
FRY	(LIKE) A CODFISH	DUDE
KISS	A PIG	COUSIN
CLIMB	MY FACE	WHY DON'T YA? (NOT ACTUALLY A MONIKER, BUT IT WORKS!)
CRY	(UP) A TREE	FELLA
USE	YOUR BRAIN	EINSTEIN
TAKE	A LONG HIKE OFF A SHORT PIER	PIERRE
HAVE	A HEART	CHUCKLEHEAD
RUN	(LIKE) THE WIND	SEÑOR

NOW *YOU* TRY IT! JUST MIX N' MATCH THE ELEMENTS FROM THESE THREE COLUMNS, AND YOU'LL HAVE A PLAYGROUND FULL OF COLORFUL PHRASEOLOGY! *MAKE SOMETHING GREAT, SCHOOLMATE!**

*THE ABOVE CATCH PHRASE, TM AND © LISA SIMPSON.

USE IT AND LOSE IT, DOOFUS!

YEAH, QUIET OR RIOT, DORK!

SILENCE OR VIOLENCE, NERD!

EAT MY STRUDEL, MEIN HERR!

KEEP YOUR B.O. TO YOURSELF, SMELLY!

TASTE MY RAINBOW, RAINBOW TASTER!

LET MY PEOPLE GO, PHARAOH!

FIGHT LIKE A CODFISH, SQUIRE!

CEASE BEHAVING LIKE LOUTS, RUFFIANS!

CRANK UP THE CRANKABLES, SOUND GUY!

67

THERE'S MORE FUN INSIDE THESE GREAT ANNUALS!

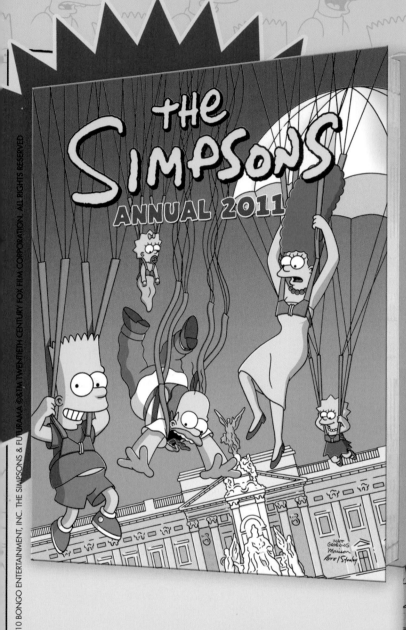

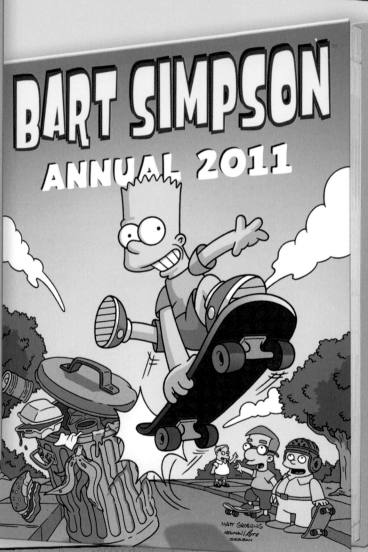

AVAILABLE NOW!

TITAN BOOKS
A WORLD OF ENTERTAINMENT

www.titanbooks.com

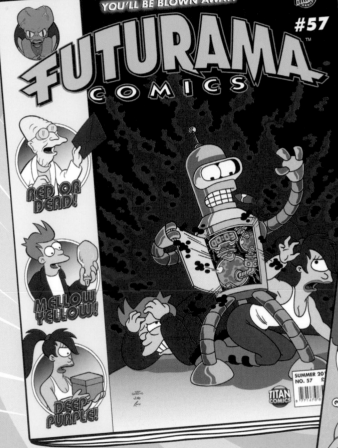